Starting Points for Science

Brenda Keogh and Stuart Naylor

Millgate House
Publishing and Consultancy Ltd

Sponsored by

bbsrc
biotechnology and biological sciences
research council

Supported by

British
Association
Promoting Science & Technology

Dedication

For Joseph Warhurst,
who combined a curiosity about the world
with a love of drawing.

He would have enjoyed this book.

Millgate House Publishers
Millgate House
30 Mill Hill Lane
Sandbach
Cheshire
CW11 4PN

Tel/Fax 01270 764314
www.millgatehouse.co.uk

First published in Great Britain in 1997. Reprinted 1999, 2002, 2005.

ISBN   0 9527506 1 9

British Library Cataloguing in Publication Data.
A catalogue record for this book is available from the British
Library.

Graphic design and typesetting by Kathryn Stawpert.

Artwork by Ged Mitchell, The Village Gallery, Wheelock,
Sandbach.

Printed by The Printing House, Marshfield Bank Employment Park,
Marshfield Bank, Crewe.

Contents

Acknowledgements

Our grateful thanks are due to all the friends and colleagues who have been involved in creating this book:

Monica Winstanley and **Tracey Reader** at the Biotechnology and Biological Sciences Research Council, for their confidence that our previous book, Scientists and Primary Schools, was a worthwhile venture and for sponsoring its publication.

Brian Gamble for his trust in our judgement and for the support provided for our work.

Kathryn Stawpert at The Manchester Metropolitan University, for translating our typed notes into a work of art.

Ged Mitchell for his illustrations and for bringing our concept cartoons to life.

Alan Goodwin at the Manchester Metropolitan University, for his constructive criticism, ideas and wise advice.

The many **colleagues**, **teachers**, **students** and **children** who have provided the inspiration and the alternative viewpoints which have resulted in the concept cartoons and who have given such helpful feedback on how the concept cartoons might be improved.

We are grateful to **Plymton St Mary C of E Infants' School**, nr Plymouth for permission to reproduce the fair test for clothes pegs from ASE Primary Science (1988) No 25.

Introduction

This book is written for teachers, student teachers and anyone else who has an interest in teaching and learning about science. It sets out some of the starting points for scientific thinking and investigation which we know can be successful with children and with adult learners. The way that we describe these starting points is deliberately kept simple - not because science is simple, but because the way that science is sometimes described can be intimidating and off-putting for learners who lack confidence.

The ideas here are a development of a previous title, **Scientists and Primary Schools**, published in 1996. That book was written to support scientists working with primary schools. It was conceived at a conference organised by the Biotechnology and Biological Sciences Research Council. Although directed to scientists it was also well received by teachers and student teachers, who found that it provided a set of accessible ideas for starting points as well as some support for their role in the classroom.

We have therefore rewritten the sections of the book which related most directly to scientists, replacing them with suggestions which are more immediately relevant to teachers and student teachers. Our aim through this book is to make science in the classroom enjoyable, productive and manageable for teachers.

The main focus of the book is on concept cartoons. Since we invented our first set of concept cartoons in 1992 we have used them regularly in our own teaching and obtained feedback from large numbers of teachers using them in their classrooms. We have been overwhelmed with the positive responses from teachers in all sectors and age ranges of the education system. This has been particularly true of teachers working with reluctant learners and children with behavioural difficulties or language difficulties. Although in this book we offer a range of starting points for science, concept cartoons appear to be one of the most valuable and effective that we have found so far.

We hope that you enjoy using them.

The teacher's role in supporting investigations

An essential feature of science in schools is that children should be enquiring in a systematic way. This will involve them in observing, exploring, investigating, researching and communicating their ideas. Through this type of enquiry they will develop the skills of working scientifically, develop their understanding of scientific ideas and begin to make sense of science as a way of finding out about the world.

Teachers of younger children frequently feel under pressure to get their children investigating as part of their first experience of science. Although their feelings may be understandable, this is an unrealistic expectation. A scientific investigation requires a degree of sophistication which very young children do not normally possess. What is much more important is to lay the foundations for scientific investigation which the children can build on as they get older. This will include exploration, along with making careful observations, beginning to work in more systematic ways and beginning to develop the concept of "fairness".

Teachers of older children may feel this pressure even more strongly. The consequences can be that the children are pushed into carrying out a systematic investigation before they have had any opportunity to sort out their own thoughts or to make sense of the situation being investigated. Exploration should be an important aspect of their science experience too. Exploration need not take a long time, but it will allow them to get a feel for the situation, to clarify their own ideas and to see the purpose in finding out more about the situation through a more systematic approach.

Some teachers have been led to believe that children will naturally investigate as long as they are given a suitable opportunity. Sometimes this can happen, but it would be foolish to rely on it. Our experience suggests that most children need considerable support in learning how to investigate effectively. The teacher therefore has a vital role in supporting the children in their investigations and in helping them to learn from their experience of science.

Some of the important aspects of the teacher's role in helping the children to investigate more effectively include the following:

- Ensure that there is a clear sense of purpose to the activity, one which is clear to the children as well as to the teacher. This means that the context for the activity needs to be carefully chosen.

- Ensure that the children are actively involved in the activity. In other words, make sure that they are intellectually engaged - minds on as well as hands on. Sometimes minds on instead of hands on may be more productive.

- Ensure that the activities are accessible to the children. The concepts involved, the language used and the context for the activity need to be suitable for the children concerned.

- Respond to the children's ideas wherever possible. They should be able to contribute their ideas at some point and feel that their ideas are relevant and valued.

- Provide a motivating stimulus for activities, one that captures the children's attention so that they want to find out more about the situation.

- Ask productive questions which direct the children's attention, stimulate their thinking and open up possibilities for exploration, investigation and research.

- Create a climate of enquiry, in which children are encouraged to ask their own questions, set their own challenges and view questions as an important aspect of their learning.

- Encourage the children to act as independent learners. This will provide the most productive setting for them to work scientifically; it will also allow the teacher to concentrate on supporting, stimulating and challenging the children rather than on organising them.

- Teach the children how to investigate. This will involve helping them to plan systematically, possibly using a planning framework supplied by the teacher, to be systematic in recording and presenting their observations, and to reflect on how they went about the investigation.

Starting points for science investigations

Everyday objects

Everyday objects can be used as starting points for investigation by highlighting some of their features and asking questions about them. Even though the object may be familiar the children will realise that they can find out more about it.

Questions such as which paper towel is best at mopping up water or which shape of cup is most stable when it is full of liquid are examples of investigations based on everyday objects. Figure 1 shows an example of an investigation into which clothes peg is the strongest. Getting each child to bring a peg from home ensures that the investigation is linked to the children's direct personal experience.

FIGURE 1

we used a dolls cup and a buckit and some sand and 3 pegs

One child put a peg on the handle of a plastic beach bucket and held it up in the air.

A second filled the cup with sand -

we smoothed off the sand with our fingers

Roland

then poured it into the bucket. *"If you pour it in gently you can get more in before the bucket falls."*

They counted the cups of sand they loaded into the bucket before it fell off the peg.

FROM ASE PRIMARY SCIENCE (1988) NO 25

Everyday events

Starting investigations from everyday events will also allow you to build on the children's personal experience and to relate new ideas to those which are already understood. Questions need to be raised which help the children to realise that their understanding of the event is incomplete.

Examples of suitable everyday events could be a kettle boiling, water evaporating from a dish of water or ice melting. Careful observation of any of these events is likely to challenge the children's thinking and make them realise that their understanding of change of state is incomplete. What is in the bubbles of boiling water, where exactly do they form, where does the water go to as the dish dries, how quickly does it evaporate and what can speed it up or slow it down are the kinds of questions that the children could investigate.

Interesting or unusual objects

In these examples the aim is to provide an object which will interest the children and hold their attention. They will naturally want to play with the object and explore what they can do with it. From here it is only a small step to investigating more systematically by focussing on specific questions about the object.

Objects which can provide interesting starting points include paper helicopters (see ASE Primary Science 1982, No 7), ice balloons (balloons filled with water and then frozen - more details in Primary Science Review 1987, No 3) or balancing toys like the one shown in Figure 2. This can be constructed simply from wooden skewers and plasticine. It will fascinate the children in the way that it can balance at almost any angle. The children will be able to develop their understanding of forces and their effects by investigating how the amount and the position of the plasticine affect the way that the model balances.

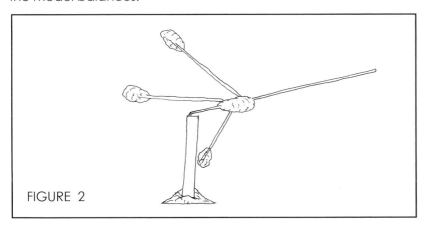

FIGURE 2

NOTE

Snip the sharp points off the skewers with a pair of scissors.

5

Interesting or unusual situations

As with the interesting or unusual objects, the aim is to provide experience of a situation that will excite the children's curiosity and hold their attention. The children's interest will lead to their asking questions and exploring the situation; questioning and exploring can then lead them into more systematic investigation.

Examples of interesting situations include the simple circuit shown in Figure 3, where pressing the switch will make the lamp go out. In Figure 4 the flattened piece of plasticine can be made to float and the flattened piece of aluminium foil made to sink. However screwing up the ball of plasticine always makes it sink while screwing up the ball of aluminium foil always makes it float!

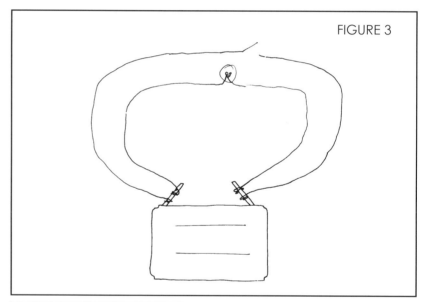

FIGURE 3

FIGURE 4

Observing the natural environment

The natural environment provides a rich resource for children's investigations. Close observation of any plant, animal or biological system will not only provide information but will also readily generate further questions. Not all the questions that children raise can be investigated. However a useful part of their learning in science is to realise that some questions are more productive and more easily investigated than others.

Examples of starting points for investigations include food preferences in animals (eg which flowers do the bees seem to prefer?), habitat preferences (eg do the woodlice seem to prefer dry or damp conditions?), plant distribution (eg which plants seem to survive best where people walk?) and seed germination (eg do the biggest seeds grow fastest?). Ideally many of the questions will come from the children themselves.

I think the bees prefer blue flowers.

....

What do you think?

Sorting and classifying

Inviting the children to decide how to sort things into groups and then to classify them using the categories that they have chosen can be a useful starting point for investigation. Classifying objects requires the children to make judgements. Frequently they will find that further investigation is necessary before these judgements can be made.

For example, inviting the children to classify materials as solids, liquids or gases can lead into investigations about viscosity. How thick can a liquid be and still be runny? Is it possible to have a runny solid? Can we find a simple measure of runniness?

Similarly classifying living things as animals or plants can lead to the children having to find out more about their characteristics. Do all animals have fur? Do all animals move? Are there any plants that move? Do all plants have roots? A set of cards with pictures of living things can generate lively discussion and provide a basis for the children wanting to investigate and find out more. Figure 5 shows some possibilities. A fascinating example of how ordinary children responded to this activity is given in *Primary Science Review* 1992, No 21.

FIGURE 5

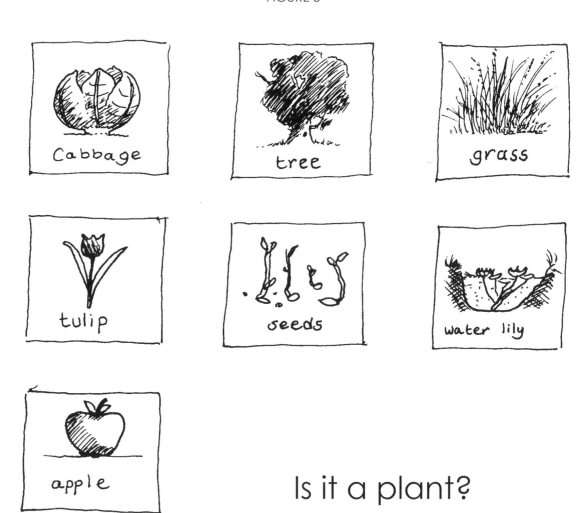

Cabbage

tree

grass

tulip

seeds

water lily

apple

Is it a plant?

Posing a problem

Posing a problem to the children can be a useful starting point. The problem involves them in a situation, and they will need to investigate the situation further in order to solve the problem. There is no shortage of problems suitable for this purpose. Publications from the Association for Science Education, including *School Science Review, Primary Science* and *Primary Science Review* are rich sources of problems that can be used in this way, so you do not need to feel that you have to invent all the problems yourself.

Some examples of suitable problems could be: -

● making a waterproof hat for Paddington Bear

● deciding on the best place to fix the school fire bell (ASE Primary Science 1989, No 28)

● making a 2-minute timer (ASE Primary Science 1988, No 25)

● investigating whether you get wetter by running or walking when it rains (ASE School Science Review 1997, No 284)

Sharing the children's ideas

Ideas may be shared informally, through writing, drawing, display or discussion for example. Alternatively a systematic technique for sharing ideas might be used, such as true/false statements, concept mapping, or listing "3 things I know about . . ." and "3 things I want to find out about . . ."

The purpose of sharing ideas in this way is to help the children to clarify their existing ideas and to identify any differences of opinion in the group. Usually children will bring very different sets of ideas and beliefs to the classroom, so sharing ideas almost always identifies numerous areas where there is debate and disagreement. These differences of opinion then provide obvious starting points for further investigation. When they realise that others may not share their beliefs, the children will usually be keen to find out more about the situation through their investigations.

For example, young children could be invited to draw themselves and their shadow. Some of the children are likely to think that their shadow will have features such as eyes and mouths, that the head is always at the top of the shadow and that the shadow is coloured, while other children may disagree. The children will quickly realise that they need to make more careful observations in order to be sure about the nature of their shadow.

Similarly older children may be invited to consider whether a balloon full of air will be heavier, lighter or the same weight as a balloon which is empty. They may come up with different answers depending on their beliefs about the nature of air as a substance. These disagreements can then lead into very productive investigations designed to resolve their differences of opinion.

Examples of other children's work

This is another way of sharing ideas by using other children's work as the focus. The children can be invited to consider the investigations carried out and the ideas put forward by other children. Evaluating their work critically can lead to other possible avenues for investigation being identified.

For example, Figure 6 shows an investigation into the strength of different types of egg boxes. It describes a thoughtful and systematic investigation with a real purpose in mind. However some children may feel that a much more realistic problem is that the egg boxes may get crushed at the bottom of a pile in the supermarket. They could carry out a systematic investigation into how resistant to crushing the different types of egg boxes are. In this way other children's work could lead to useful follow-up investigations.

Examples of other children's work might be obtained from other classes in the school, from displays, from colleagues in other schools, from publications such as ASE Primary Science or from the internet.

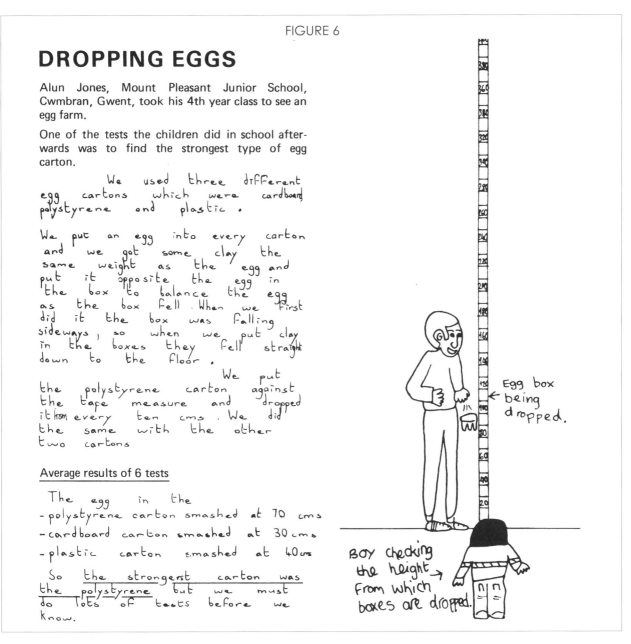

FIGURE 6

DROPPING EGGS

Alun Jones, Mount Pleasant Junior School, Cwmbran, Gwent, took his 4th year class to see an egg farm.

One of the tests the children did in school afterwards was to find the strongest type of egg carton.

We used three different egg cartons which were cardboard polystyrene and plastic.

We put an egg into every carton and we got some clay the same weight as the egg and put it opposite the egg in the box to balance the egg as the box fell. When we first did it the box was falling sideways, so when we put clay in the boxes they fell straight down to the floor.

We put the polystyrene carton against the tape measure and dropped it from every ten cms. We did the same with the other two cartons

Average results of 6 tests

The egg in the
- polystyrene carton smashed at 70 cms
- cardboard carton smashed at 30 cms
- plastic carton smashed at 40 cms

So the strongest carton was the polystyrene but we must do lots of tests before we know.

Egg box being dropped.

Boy checking the height from which boxes are dropped.

FROM ASE PRIMARY SCIENCE (1981) NUMBER 6

11

Concept cartoons

Concept cartoons are cartoon-style drawings which illustrate possible areas of uncertainty in everyday situations.

Each concept cartoon presents the children with alternative viewpoints on some scientific concept. They invite the children to share their views and to explore which of the alternatives presented is more likely to be correct. In some cases discussion may be sufficient for the children to develop their ideas, but usually the children will be desperate to start investigating to find out more about the situation presented in the concept cartoon! Through investigation they will be able to develop their ideas further.

The concept cartoons are not necessarily designed to have a single right answer. In many cases the only possible answer is "It depends on . . . ." This is a realistic perspective on science for the children to develop. Most of the concept cartoons can lead to a wide range of possible investigations, with the children's initial ideas determining which investigation will be most relevant to them.

Concept cartoons work well with adults as well as children

The concept cartoons can be copied and given to the children or they could be redrawn much larger and used as a focus for a group or class discussion. Having small groups of children working on a concept cartoon together is usually the most effective arrangement. However they can also be a useful starting point for an individual project or as an extra challenge to some of the children.

The concept cartoons can be a very powerful means of providing starting points for investigation, particularly for children who have poor literacy skills, who lack confidence in science or who are reluctant learners. We have therefore included 30 examples of concept cartoons, covering a wide range of aspects of science, along with suggestions for the kinds of investigations which may emerge from them.

Other possibilities

There are lots of other possible starting points for investigations. These include resources in or around the school which can provide starting points, such as stories, workschemes and the school environment. Other starting points for investigations can come from the local or national news, from the weather, from a trip round a supermarket or from a visit by the children to a local industry or community organisation (such as a local charity) where this is feasible. A creative imagination and a willingness to allow the children to generate their own questions and ideas will usually be sufficient for developing worthwhile investigations

Concept cartoons as starting points

Living things and life processes

Plant in water

There are several issues in this concept cartoon. Some of the children will be surprised that plants can grow new roots, unlike humans, rabbits or birds which cannot normally replace damaged bits of their bodies. They may be surprised that plants can manage without roots as long as they have a good water supply. They may be surprised that plants can manage without an obvious supply of food, since they may well believe that plants take in food from the soil through their roots. They can investigate each of these ideas and begin to lay the foundation for more complex ideas about plant structure, function, growth and feeding.

Seeds and cotton wool

Sometimes incidental factors can seem very important to the children. If they germinate seeds on cotton wool they may not have a clear idea of what the cotton wool (or paper towel or tissue or sponge or . . .) is for. They may not realise that any material which traps water would work just as well as cotton wool. The children can investigate the various possibilities put forward in the concept cartoon by adjusting each of the factors separately.

New growth

Identifying where new growth occurs in plants is not obvious to children. The concept cartoon invites them to observe plants closely and to investigate where the new growth takes place. Part of the children's investigation will involve deciding how they will be able to spot the new growth when it happens. They may come up with ideas such as making detailed drawings, taking photographs, marking the plant at regular intervals or looking for differences in appearance between new plant tissue and old. They will be surprised to find out that the new growth is not always in the same place on a plant. For example, although most plants grow from the tip of the shoot, grasses grow from the base of the shoot which is why they carry on growing after cutting a lawn.

Many biological investigations do not allow "experiments" to be set up to observe the effect of changing one of the factors. Sometimes we can only examine a biological system carefully and attempt to identify relationships which may be present. This is the case with the runners. The children can look for a correlation between how fast children can run and the other factors suggested in the cartoon. They would need to collect data systematically in order to identify any possible link. They may well discover that none of the factors shown makes any difference to the running speed. The genetic link between children and their parents is mentioned as one possibility. It is important to treat any questions about the children's family backgrounds with sensitivity and not to make assumptions about their backgrounds.

Runners

The children might expect that rate of growth will depend on seed size. They might expect small seeds (eg cress) to germinate quickly, bigger seeds (eg beans) to take a few days and very large seeds (eg avocado) to take ages. However there are plenty of examples which don't fit this pattern, such as parsley seeds which are small and can take months to germinate. An investigation using different sized seeds can easily be set up. Seeds of the same type will tend to germinate at roughly similar rates, though individual seeds can vary greatly. Other factors can also be investigated, such as the shape of the seed, how wrinkly it is and how thick the outer coat is. The meaning of "growing faster" can also be investigated - the time taken for the first root to appear, the rate of growth of the root and the rate of vertical growth of the shoot are all possibilities.

Size of seeds

Often children will only identify mammals as animals, with rapid movement on four legs usually being their most significant feature. They may believe that if something is an animal then it cannot also be in another group. They will not realise that birds, fish and insects are animals as well as being birds, fish and insects. "Animal" is an inclusive category, rather than an exclusive one. This concept cartoon invites the children to rethink their existing definition and to look for a consistent meaning for the word.

Is it an animal?

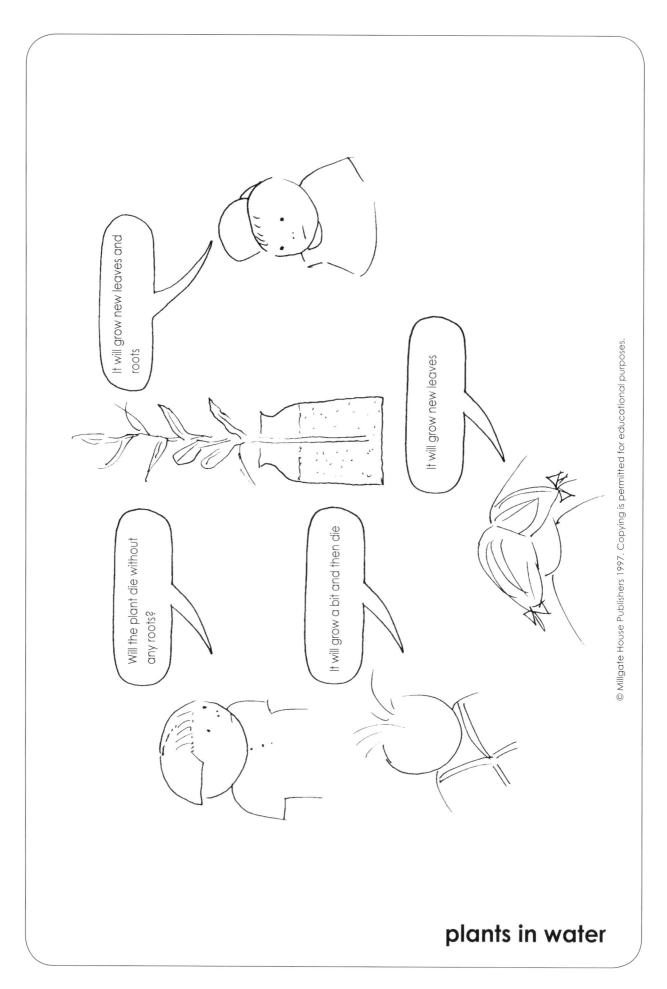

plants in water

seeds and cotton wool

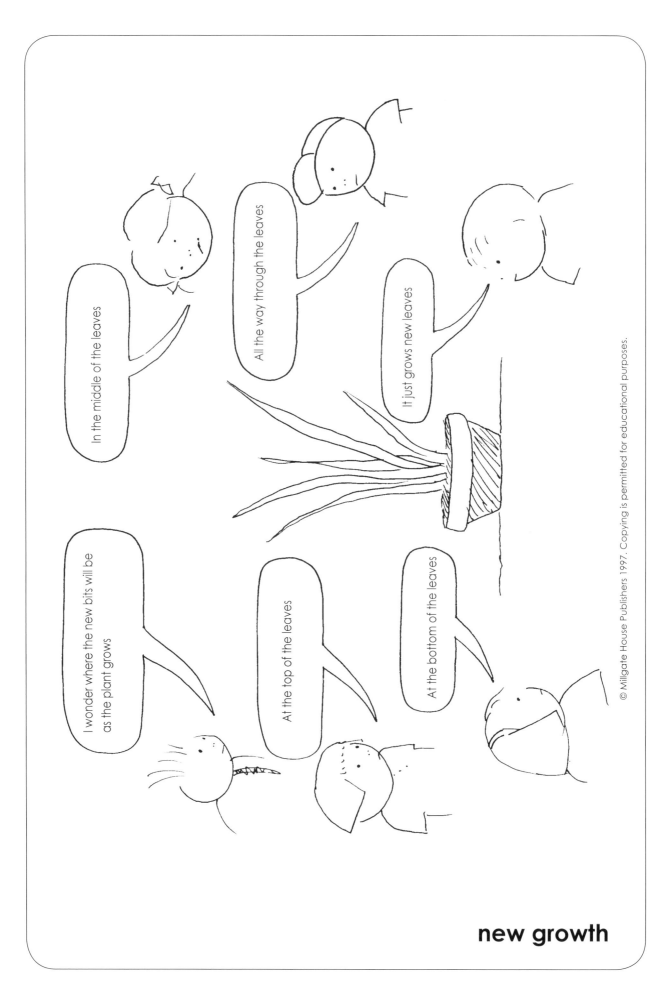

new growth

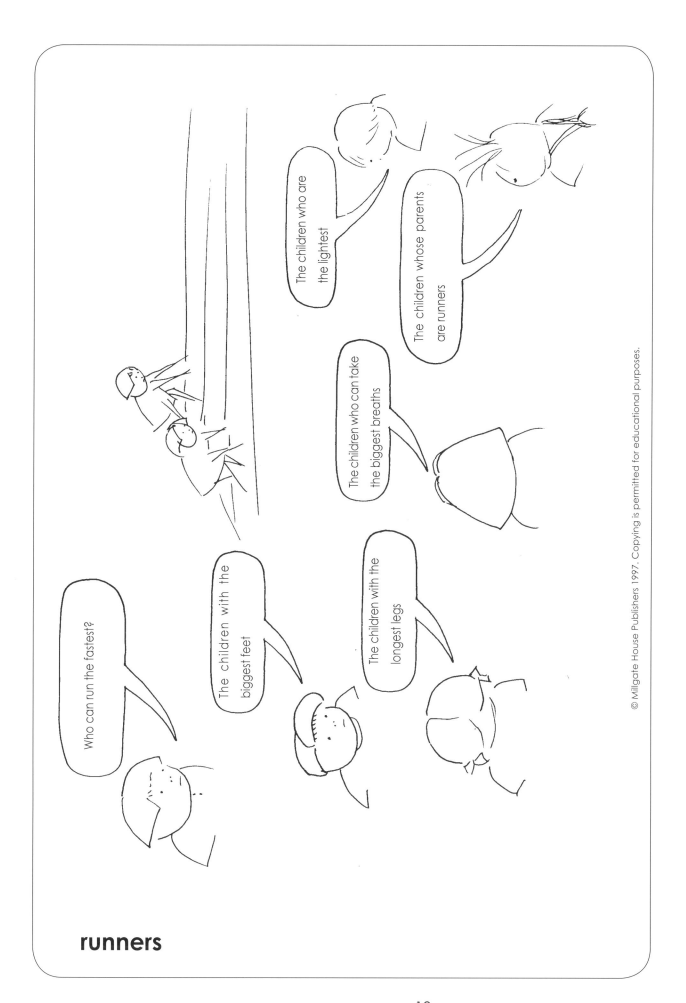

runners

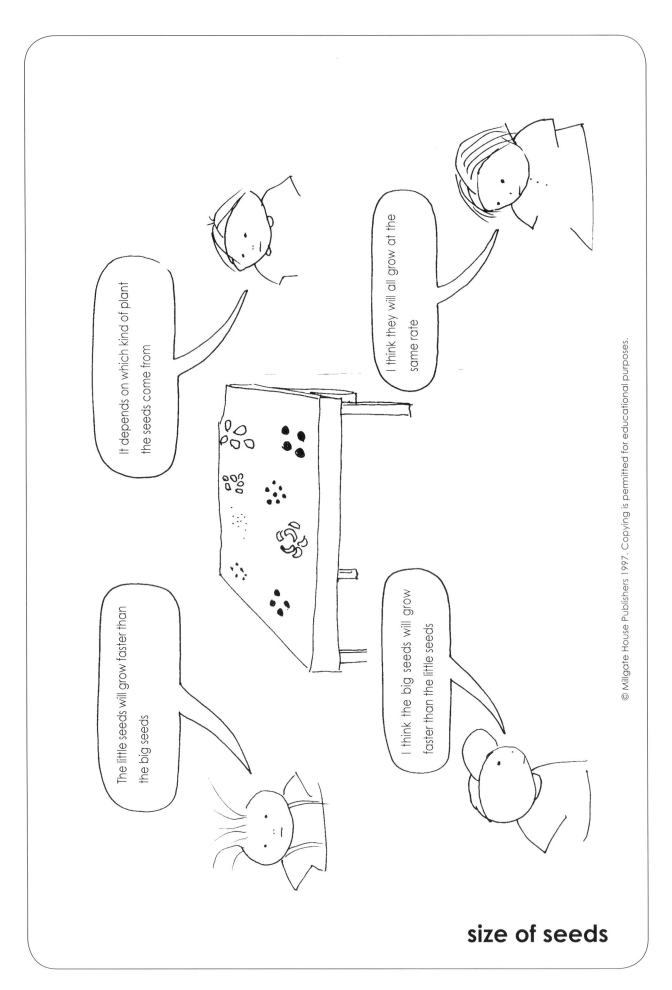

size of seeds

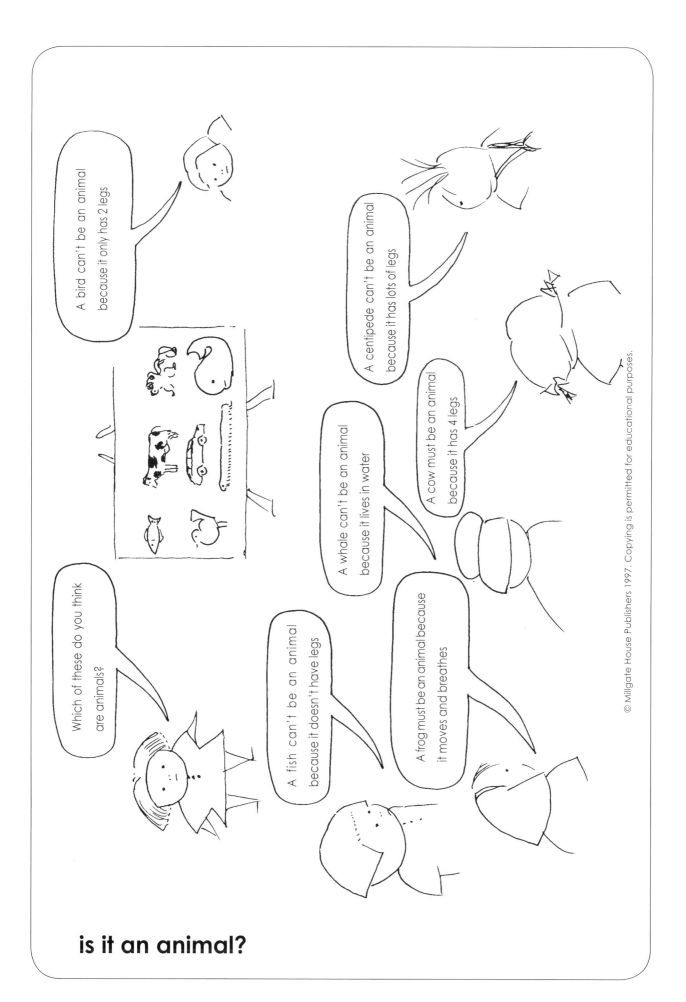

is it an animal?

Light and shadows

Cards and shadows

The issue in this concept cartoon is whether shadows are affected by the colour or thickness of an object. Since a shadow is simply the absence of light, any object that blocks the path of light can make a shadow. As long as the light is completely blocked, the nature of the object will not make any difference to the shadow. It will be fairly straightforward for children to investigate the shadows formed by cards of different thicknesses and colours, as shown in the concept cartoon, in order to show that the nature of the object does not normally make any difference to the shadow. However the investigation may be complicated by a number of factors. If the card has a shiny surface which reflects the light, if light comes from more than one source, or if the card is thin enough to let light through then the intensity and colour of the shadows may be affected. Access to a light meter or light sensor could be useful for the older children.

Shadow stick

The issue here is the position of the sun rather than anything to do with the stick. Observing the stick's shadow at different times of day will reveal that the shadow changes its length and position as the sun moves. This can be a lead in to further investigations about how the sun moves and how this changes during the year. Making a simple sundial could be a useful follow up activity. Other investigations could focus on the relationship between the light source and the object, where the intensity of the source or the distance and the angle between the source and object can be altered.

Bending mirror

Precisely how curved mirrors reflect light is complex. Children are unlikely to understand the concepts involved in any depth. However it is possible for them to investigate this situation systematically and to gain a better understanding of the various ways in which images can be formed. By using a flexible plastic mirror they can investigate the differences between reflections in concave and convex mirrors and the difference that the degree of curvature makes to the size of the reflected image. Setting up a fairground hall of mirrors will be an enjoyable way for the children to apply their understanding.

There is a strong possibility of confusion between the distance that the light travels and how well a light source illuminates an object. The children are unlikely to realise that the light travels the same distance regardless of whether it is day or night. This is not easy to prove. They could set up investigations such as testing whether they can see a small torch shining from a distance at different times of day when background illumination varies. This should help them to realise that the light from the torch still travels to an observer even in bright sunlight. Understanding that we see because light from a source enters our eyes is necessary for this to be a meaningful investigation. Separate investigations could be carried out into how well a torch beam illuminates an object in conditions of different background lighting. A useful follow up could be to investigate how to make objects highly visible (eg road signs) and how to make them invisible (eg animals being camouflaged to avoid predators).

Headlights at night

cards and shadows

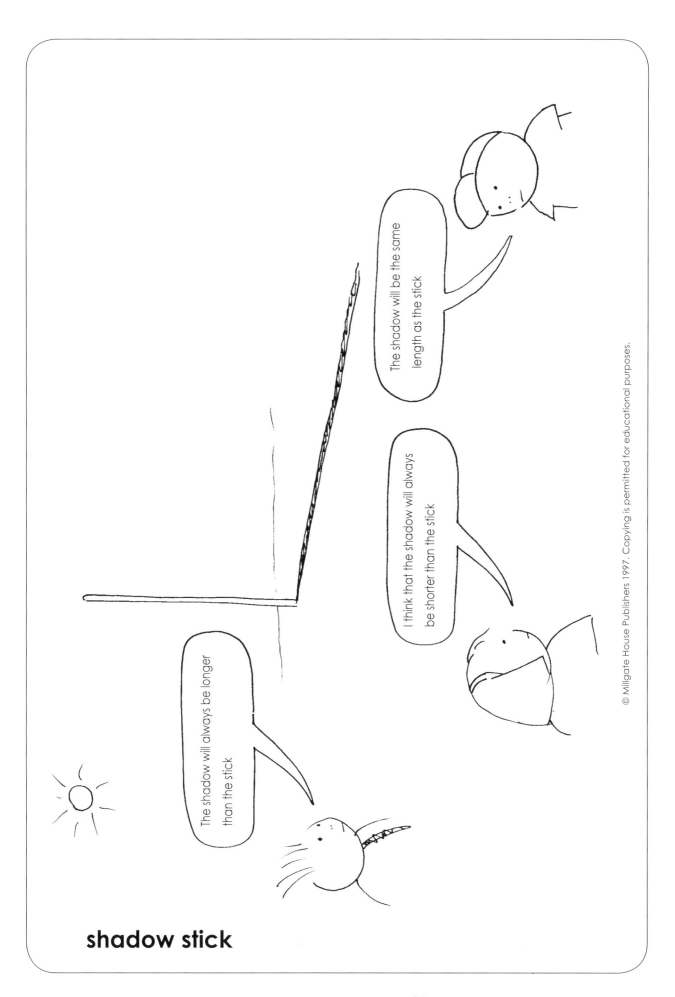

shadow stick

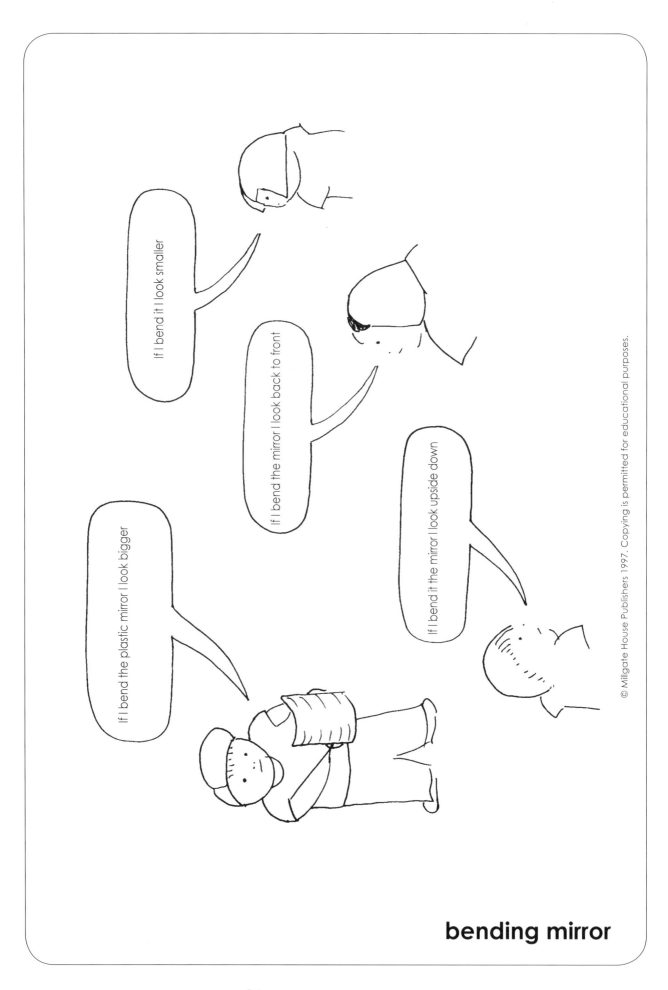

bending mirror

headlights at night

Materials

Snowman   The issue in this concept cartoon is whether the coat is an insulator or whether it actually generates heat. Some children may believe that warm clothes make you warmer by making more heat, and they will expect the coat to generate heat and melt the snowman faster. However others will realise that the coat is simply an insulator which will tend to keep heat away from the snowman and prevent it from melting quickly. The situation shown in the concept cartoon can be investigated using real snow. Alternatively it can be modelled with ice inside a coat, glove or sock; the top half of a plastic mineral water bottle, filled with water and frozen, will make a good model snowman. The thickness, colour and nature of the material that the coat is made from can also be investigated.

Ice pops   All of the predictions in this concept cartoon can be directly investigated by the children. Some of them are likely to think that aluminium foil is an insulator; that cotton wool makes things warmer; that water will keep the ice pop cold; and that things will stay frozen inside a refrigerator. In each case they will be surprised by their observations! This can lead on to a whole series of follow up investigations on conductors, insulators and heat transfer.

Ice cream   Although the children will have experience of condensation they are unlikely to have well-formed ideas about where the condensed water comes from. The concept cartoon invites them to consider and investigate a number of possibilities, and they may well think of other possibilities themselves. The fact that the condensation comes from the air may appear to be the least likely possibility to many of the children. Wrapping the ice cream tub in polythene or aluminium foil and observing where the condensation forms should help to clarify their ideas. Investigations such as this help to lay the foundation for later work on the structure of matter and conservation of mass.

The children will have intuitive ideas about what they mean by a solid. However they will not find it easy to apply their ideas in a consistent way. They will find it difficult to separate the object from the material it is made from, and they will tend to associate properties such as heaviness and rigidity with solids. The concept cartoon provides an opportunity for them to rethink their definitions and to make more systematic judgements. Introducing more challenging materials such as sand or dough is probably best left until after their ideas about solids are reasonably well developed.

Is it a solid?

The distinction between melting and dissolving is a common area of confusion for children. They can clarify the meaning they attach to both of these terms by investigating the situation shown in the concept cartoon. A tray full of sand can be used to model the effect of the tide on sand-castles. Observation of other changes in materials, such as melting chocolate or dissolving sugar, will be a useful complement to their investigation.

Sand-castles

This concept cartoon invites the children to reverse the familiar process of dissolving. It also challenges the children's ideas about what happens to the sugar in the tea - does it disappear completely as it dissolves or can it be recovered from the tea? The children can investigate the possibilities shown in the concept cartoon as well as other possibilities that they might suggest. Salt is a useful alternative, since it can be separated more easily from water than the sugar. Other means of separating materials would be useful ways to follow up this investigation.

Sugar in tea

snowman

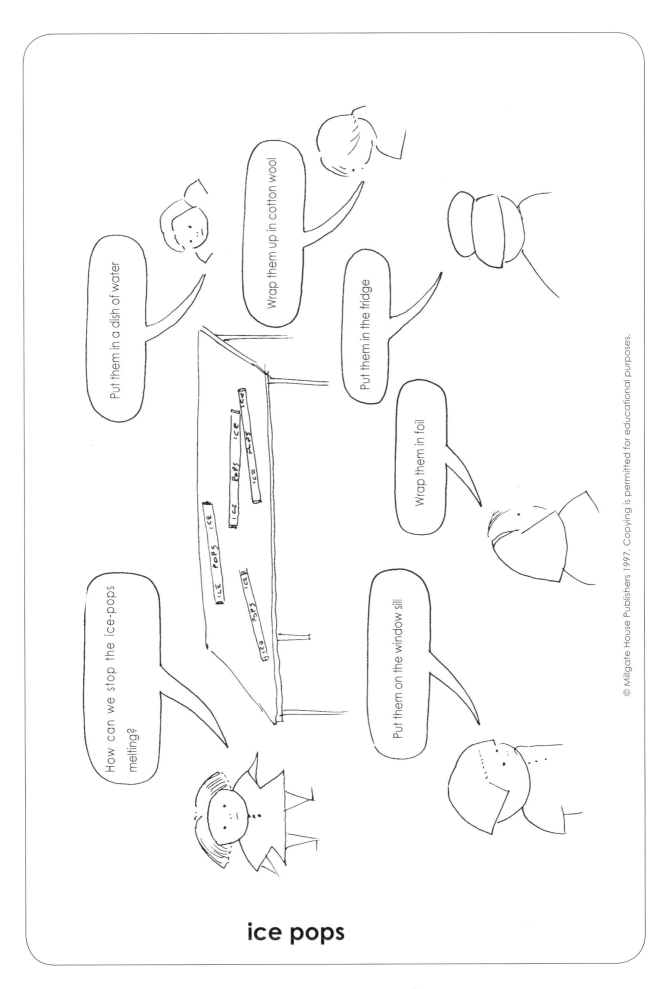

ice pops

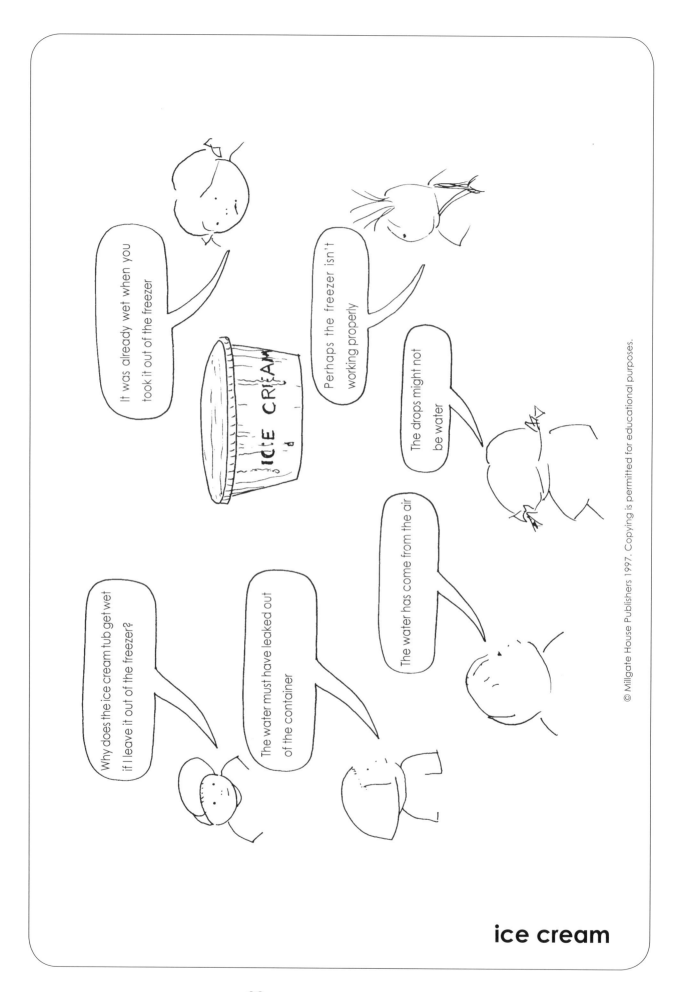

ice cream

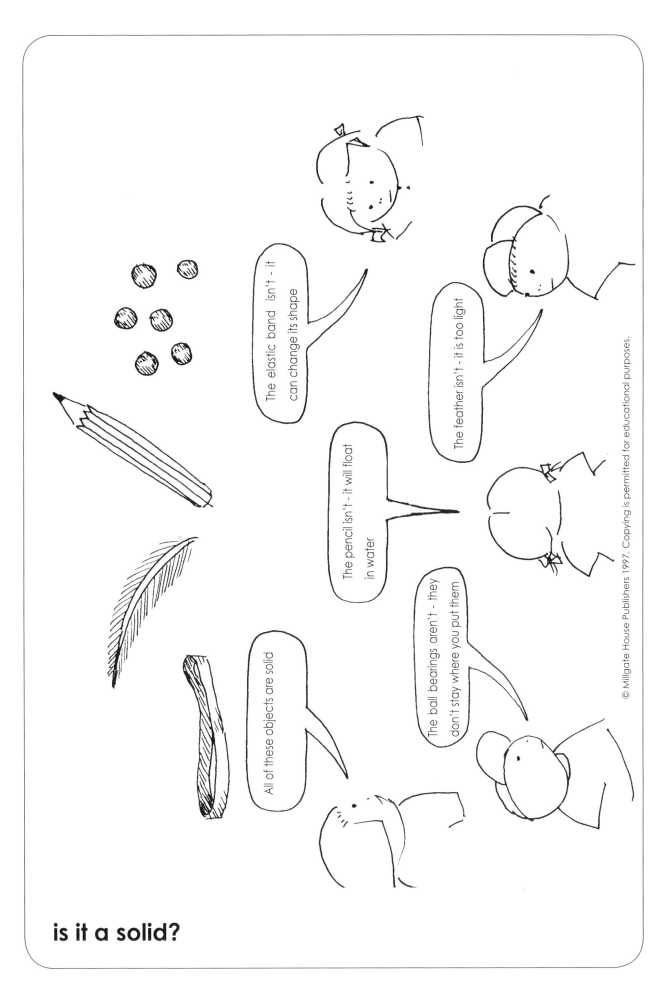

is it a solid?

sand-castles

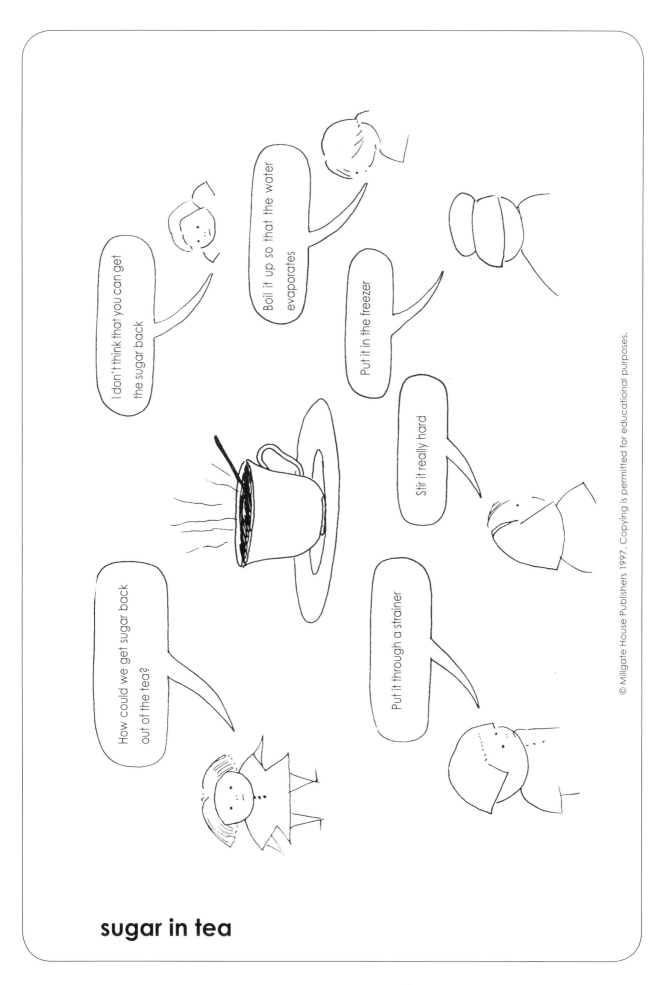

sugar in tea

Sound and hearing

Big ears

This concept cartoon invites children to investigate whether ear size makes any difference to the ability to hear quiet sounds and to judge the direction of a sound. Each of these can be investigated separately. The children can make themselves large ears out of card for their investigation and can close their eyes while they listen to sounds being made by other children. You may need to find a quiet area for this to be manageable. The children's investigations can lead in to follow up work which looks at the ears of animals in real life and relates the size of ears to life style. Useful examples of the importance of large ears are seen in some hunting animals (eg owl), hunted animals (eg rabbit) and animals that navigate by sound (eg bat). Large ears can also serve other functions, such as helping to keep an animal cool (eg elephant).

Guitar string

The guitar string provides a manageable way to investigate how the thickness of a string affects the nature of the sound produced. The children will quickly realise that the length and tension in the string also make a difference. These need to be kept constant as far as possible during the children's investigations. Their results should be applicable to any stretched string, so they should be able to make their own instrument from elastic bands stretched over a hollow container. If they understand some of the general relationships (such as bigger objects tend to make lower-pitched sounds) then they may be able to apply these to other musical instruments. Some of these other instruments could be modelled, using bottles or tubes to model organ pipes, plant pots to model bells, and so on.

String telephone

This concept cartoon identifies several factors which might affect the way that sound is transmitted. All of them can be investigated by the children with very limited apparatus. Their investigations should begin to develop their ideas on sound transmission and sound amplification. This can lead in to further investigations on how well sound is transmitted by different materials, how well sound is transferred from one medium to another and how the shape of an object can affect sound transmission.

This concept cartoon illustrates a possible area of confusion between glass as a material and a glass as an object. Glass windows act as a reasonable sound insulator because sounds are not trransmitted well from air to glass. Double glazing, with a layer of air between two sheets of glass, is even more effective because of the extra layer of air. However holding a glass to the wall allows the sound to travel directly from the wall through the glass without having to travel through the air as well. The shape of the glass also helps to amplify the sound.   Investigating how different shaped objects can transmit or amplify sound and what kinds of materials make good sound insulators will help to develop the children's ideas. Older children may find that a sound sensor is a useful aid to their investigation. The children's investigations can easily be related to real-life situations where sound transmission or insulation are important, such as soundproofing a noisy teenager's bedroom or ensuring that the fire bell can be heard all the way round the school.

Glass to the wall

big ears

guitar string

string telephone

glass on wall

Living things and their environment

Plants use up soil

In this concept cartoon the issue is whether plants obtain their food from the soil, with obvious consequences for the soil level. The children can investigate plants growing in varying amounts of soil, including no soil at all, and measure any apparent changes in the soil level. They will be surprised to discover that the soil level does not go down noticeably and that the plant must get its food from somewhere other than the soil. The suggestion that some changes may be too small to notice introduces a degree of tentativeness into their thinking. Whether the plants use up soil can lead in to the more fundamental question of how plants do obtain their food. The idea that energy from sunlight allows plants to manufacture their own food is not intuitively obvious. Preparatory work on particle theory and conservation of mass may well be necessary before the children can make much sense of this idea.

Rubbish bin

This concept cartoon links recycling and rotting. The children will probably not be aware of the difference between deliberate recycling - usually involving breaking down the object into simpler raw materials that can be reused - and rotting, when organic materials naturally decompose under the action of bacteria and moulds. They can investigate whether a range of items will decompose over a period of time and they will need to take into account the conditions which are likely to lead to decomposition. It will be useful to draw a distinction between organic ("made from something that used to be a part of a living thing") and inorganic in their investigation. Care should be taken with sharp edges on the cans and the risk of breakage to the glass; some schools will not allow children to handle glass.

Leaves in woodland

The children can set up investigations to explore whether leaves decompose or whether they are eaten by a variety of invertebrates. In this concept cartoon the possibilities are not mutually exclusive and they will all occur in natural circumstances such as a woodland. Either possibility can be a useful introduction to understanding how natural cycles work. The children will need to consider what the conditions are like when leaves fall off the trees and they will need to find some way of preventing leaves from blowing away so that invertebrates can eat them.

The possibilities in this concept cartoon are not mutually exclusive. Breeding, breathing, protection and eating are all good reasons why frogs prefer to be near water much of the time. It would be extremely difficult for the children to carry out a practical investigation into this situation. Instead they will need to research different aspects of the frog's life history and make judgements based on the information available to them. They may appreciate some pointers, such as finding out what herons eat or finding out what eats worms, slugs and beetles.

Crowding and competition for light, water and nutrients from the soil are all reasons why plants do not grow in certain places. Some plants, including many conifers, also produce carpets of slowly-decaying leaves which can prevent other plants from growing. The children may be able to identify other situations where plants do not grow under trees. If they can then this may be a better focus for a practical investigation. It is possible for them to investigate some of the factors mentioned by growing plants in pots under the trees and by growing plants in soil taken from under the trees. It is unlikely that any investigation will provide conclusive proof since a number of these factors are likely to interact in real life.

This concept cartoon presents a number of possibilities as to why there are more weeds than vegetables in the vegetable patch. Each of them can be investigated separately. It is quite likely that all of the factors mentioned could be important, as well as other factors such as the effects of drought, slugs or disease. Careful observation will show that not all weeds grow quickly. However many common weeds are opportunist species with short life cycles so that they can germinate, grow and produce seeds in a few weeks. Other weeds with longer life cycles might be more able to cope with poor growing conditions. Other factors might also apply, such as the ability of some plants to reproduce by underground stems or roots or from bits of plant left in the ground after weeding the vegetable patch.

Frogs and mud

Fir trees

Weeds and vegetables

43

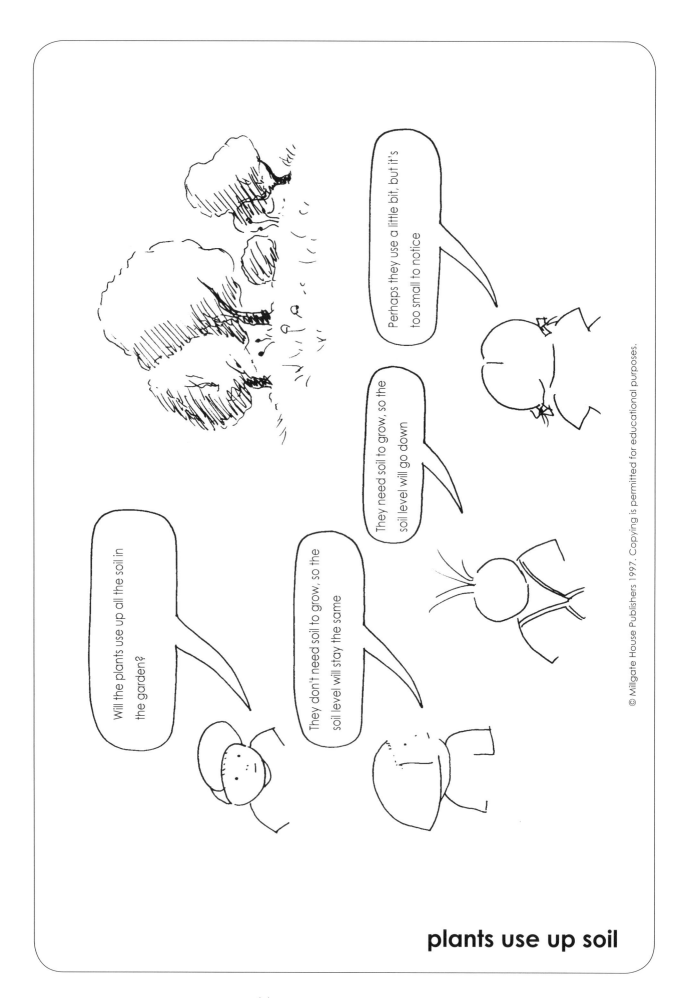

plants use up soil

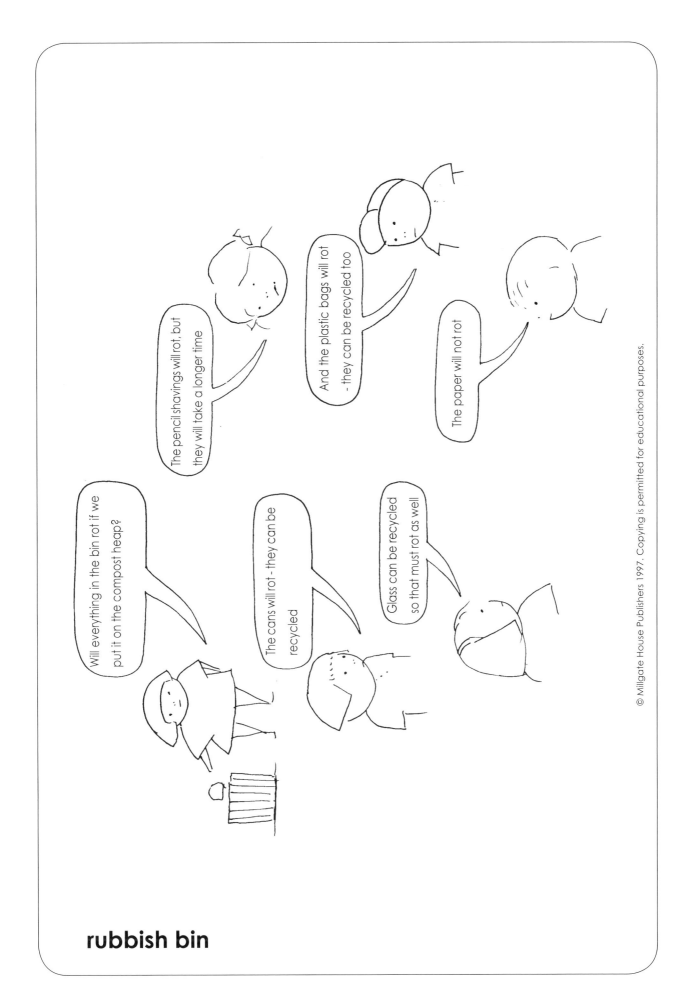

rubbish bin

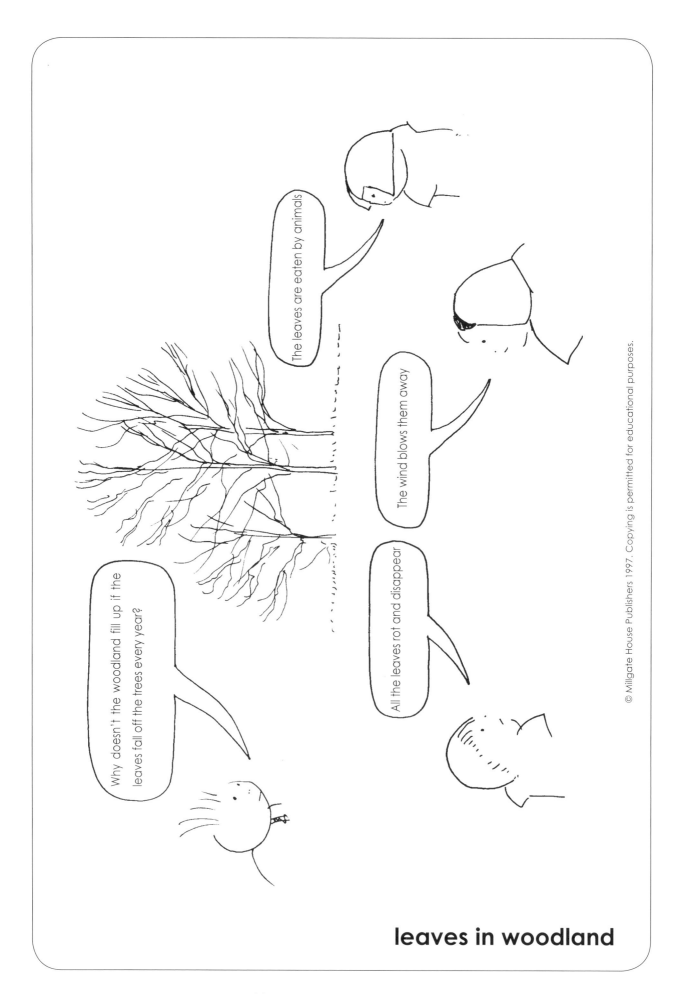

leaves in woodland

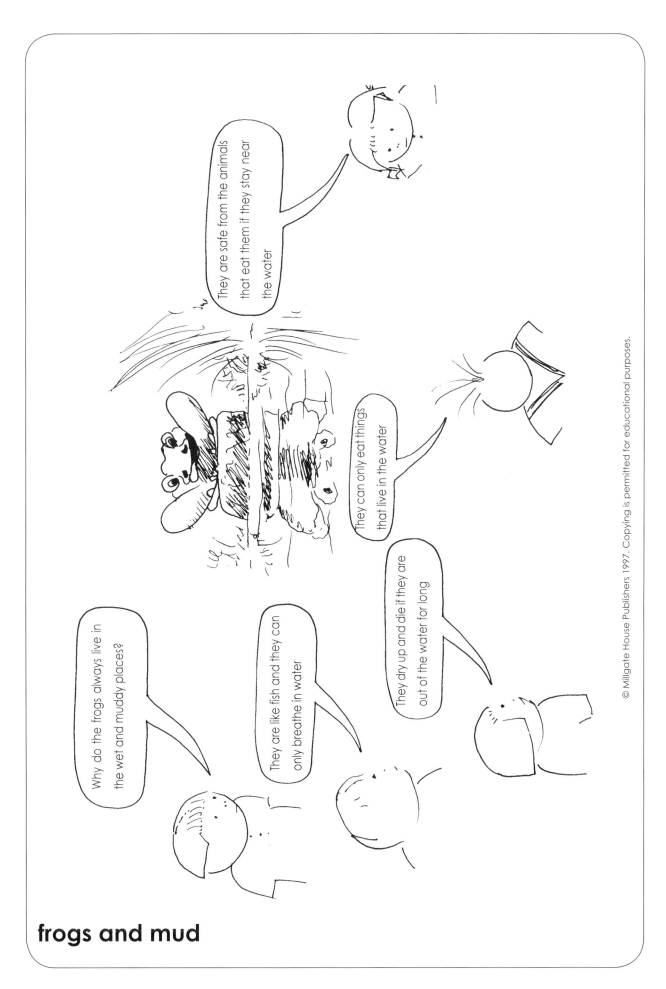

frogs and mud

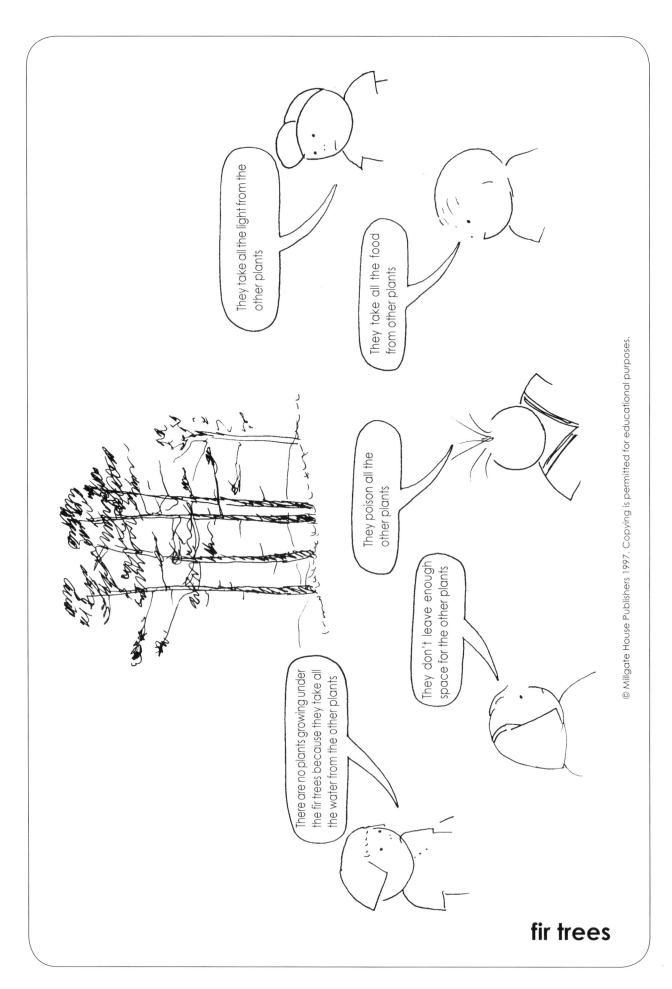

fir trees

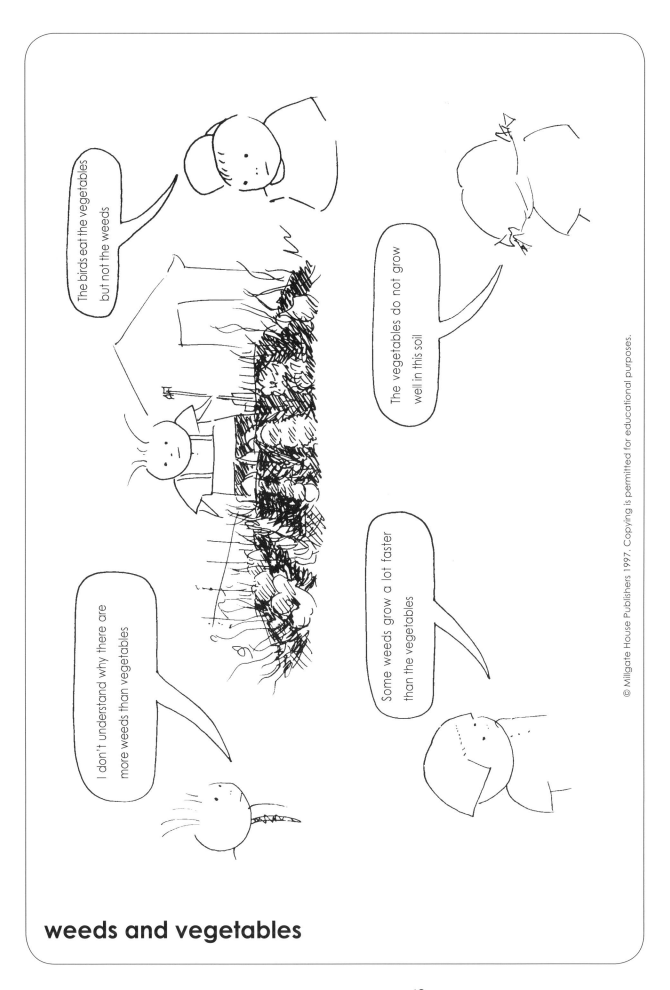

weeds and vegetables

Forces

Dropping objects

This concept cartoon illustrates the question of whether the weight of an object affects the speed at which it falls. This can be investigated directly by the children. Other factors such as the size and shape of the falling objects can also be investigated. They will probably be surprised to discover that gravity has the same effect on all objects and that generally the weight of an object makes no noticeable difference to how quickly it falls. Gravity attracts heavy and light objects towards the earth at the same rate. A useful follow on is for the children to investigate how quickly objects with a large surface area fall (eg parachutes). Other investigations can focus on the speed of falling of objects which are light for their size (eg polystyrene blocks) and on how to increase or decrease the speed of falling. These further investigations will help to develop their understanding of how the effect of air resistance can be significant in determining how quickly an object falls.

Bathroom scales

The issue in this concept cartoon is the relationship between weight and pressure. The children may not realise that there is a distinction between them. In this situation the girl's weight will not change if she stands on one leg or two, but the pressure under her foot will change since her weight will be spread over a different sized area. Investigating the situation shown will demonstrate how weight and pressure are different. A similar situation can be investigated using a block of wood pressing down on plasticine. The depth of the indentation in the plasticine will indicate the pressure under the wood. Putting weights on the block of wood will increase the pressure and cause a bigger indentation. Changing the size of the block of wood will also alter the pressure and affect the depth of the indentation, even though the weight has not changed. This connection between weight and pressure has many real life applications, including snowshoes, roof ladders and stiletto heeled shoes.

Here the question of how friction affects sliding is important. The children will have developed intuitive ideas about friction and its effects from their everyday experience. This concept cartoon invites them to develop their ideas in a more systematic way. All of the factors shown in the concept cartoon can be investigated by the children. They can explore the effect of the size, shape and weight of the block on sliding; they can alter the size of the frictional force by using smoother or rougher surfaces and by using various lubricants. The effect of most of the factors is fairly predictable, but the fact that the weight of the block makes no noticeable diffence to how it slides may be surprising. They may also identify other features as important, such as the angle or length of the ramp. In order to be meaningful they will need to keep all these other factors constant as they investigate one of the factors involved. This situation provides a useful opportunity to consolidate the children's ideas on how to carry out a fair test.

Wood on ramp

The issue in this concept cartoon is whether the depth of water affects the way that an object floats. Some of the children may be surprised that the depth of the water doesn't make any difference to the way that the boat floats. Even though ships sail all round the world it is quite common for them to believe that the depth of water makes a difference, just as many of them believe that they will be more likely to sink in the deep end of the swimming pool. The situation shown in the concept cartoon can be investigated using tanks or bowls of water. Simple boats can be made from folded aluminium foil and the way that the boat floats in different depths of water can be observed. Other factors can affect the way that the boat floats, such as how much weight there is in the boat, the shape and size of the boat, the material it is made from and whether it contains air. These will need to be taken into account when investigating the effect of depth, and they can all be investigated separately to extend understanding further.

Boat in deep water

dropping objects

bathroom scales

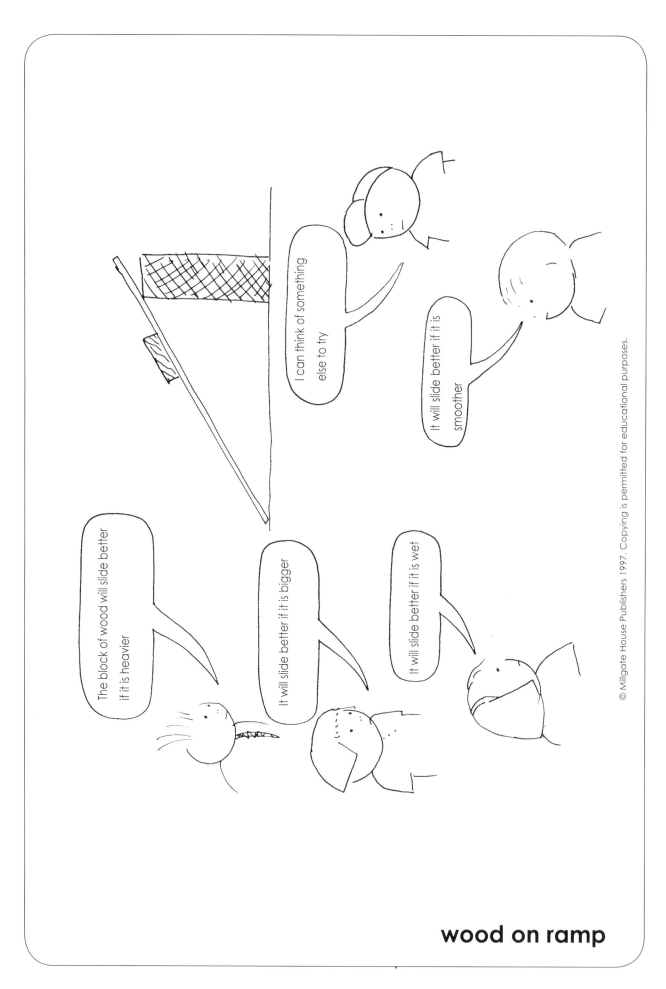

wood on ramp

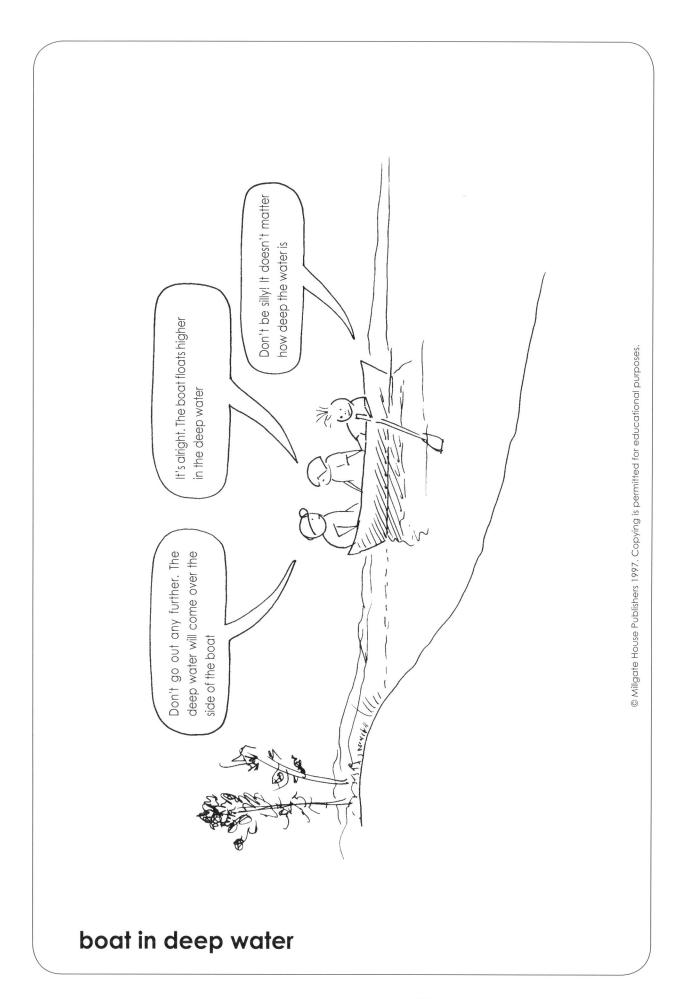

boat in deep water

Biographical notes

Brenda Keogh started her professional career as a primary teacher in 1972. Since then she has worked as a lab technician, resources officer, advisory teacher, national curriculum coordinator and lecturer in science eduactation.

Stuart Naylor started his professional career as a secondary teacher in 1971. Since then he has worked as a lab technician and advisory teacher as well as teaching in the USA. He lectured in science education at the Didsbury School of Education at Manchester Metropolitan University.

Brenda and Stuart both have extensive experience in teacher education. They share a wide range of professional interests and work together in promoting effective teaching strategies, making science enjoyable and valuing the commitment and professionalism of teachers. They work with an extensive network of individuals, groups and organisations to promote the public understanding of science. They recently founded Millgate House Publishers as a means of making their innovative work on concept cartoons more widely available.